First Words with Peppa Pig

Level 2

Mr Fox's Van

Based on the Peppa Pig TV series

Peppa

Freddy Fox

Mr Fox

Learn

all at be black did do have

new there they under want white

things

banjo

Est. 2010

rope

petrol

bike

3

Freddy Fox had a new bike and a new hat. The hat was black and white.

Freddy went to see Peppa with the new bike and the new hat. He put on the black and white hat.

"I have a new bike and a new black and white
hat. They came from my dad's van," said Freddy Fox.
"Do you have a bell on the bike?" said Peppa.

"No. If I want a bell, my dad will have a new
one in the van," said Freddy Fox.
Mr Fox has a lot of things in his van.

They went to find Mr Fox's van.
Mr Fox did have a new bell in the van.

"I had a bell at the back under the hats," said Mr Fox.
"If you want a new thing, there will be one in the van!"

Est. 2010

"Do you have a cup in the van?" said Peppa.
Mr Fox did have a cup in there. Mr Fox had lots
of cups at the back under the bikes.

"You have a lot of things in the van," they all said. "If you want a new thing, there will be one in the van!" said Mr Fox.

Est. 2010

"Do you have a banjo in the van?" said Peppa.
Mr Fox did have a banjo at the back under the cups.

"You have a lot of things in there," they all said. "If you want a new thing, there will be one in the van!" said Mr Fox.

"Do you have a tree in the van?" said Peppa.
Mr Fox did have a tree in the van.
"Do you want this tree? It was at the back
under the lamp," said Mr Fox.

"You have a lot of things in there," they all said.
"If you want a new thing, there will be one in
the van!" said Mr Fox.

"Do you have a hen in the van?" said Peppa.
Mr Fox did have a hen in the van.
"I have got this black hen in a white box. It was at the back under the clock," said Mr Fox.
"You have a lot of things in there," they all said.
"If you want a new thing, there will be one in the van!" said Mr Fox.

Mr Fox and Freddy
went to the van.

Est. 2010

"Mr Fox has a lot of things in the van," said Peppa. "If you want a new thing, there will be one in the van!" they all said.

The van did not go. One thing Mr Fox did not have in the van was petrol.

"Do you have a rope in the van?" said Peppa.
Mr Fox did have a rope in the van.

"I have a lot of things in the van, but
I must have petrol, too!" said Mr Fox.

What next?

Peek under this flap for a fun game to practise the words you have just read in the story!

Can you **make up a story** about Peppa and her family?

Est. 2010

Draw **a picture** of the inside of Mr Fox's van. What other interesting things does he have inside?

Use some objects from home to **make your own pretend shop**. Your friends or family could be customers!

at
2 points

there
1 point

they
2 points

do
3 points

under
3 points

want
3 points

black
1 point

white
1 point

new
2 points

did
1 point

be
3 points

all
1 point

have
2 points